In the centuries between the drowning of ATLANTIS and the founding of JERICHO, another civilization arose in another part of the world--nine gleaming citadels wrought from desert stone and sand.

Each was a kingdom unto itself, at war with all the others... until the coming of the DARK LORDS.

They were SORCERERS--called Koth, Hemuth, Eeyod, and Zepharr--and were said to be survivors of the lost continent, possessors of its esoteric secrets. They met and conquered nine mighty armies, vanquishing all resistance with the FIRE from their HANDS.

They UNITED the citadels in SERVITUDE. And from the ebon towers of their stronghold, called KUR, the Dark Lords ruled for a thousand years.

Now, however, their empire is in DECLINE.

Published by The Marvel Comics Group; 387 Park Avenue So; New York, NY 10016.   **ISBN #0-87135-001-7**

A MARVEL GRAPHIC NOVEL™
by STEVE GERBER and VAL MAYERIK

Void Indigo

BOOK ONE:
Tortured Souls

EROK... HAS FALLEN TO ATH'AGAAR.

AS DID TZERAMA.

AS DID BAALAT.

AS DID KEREI.

HOW LONG HAVE WE... ERE THE BARBARIANS MOUNT AN ASSAULT ON KUR ITSELF?

THE TRUTH, MY BROTHERS, IS THAT WE ARE OLD. OUR STRENGTH WANES...

...AND WITH IT, OUR CONTROL OVER THE ARCANE FORCES WHICH IN THE PAST ENSURED OUR SUPREMACY.

AGE HAS NOT SAPPED YOUR TALENT FOR CANDOR, HAS IT, KOTH?

WHAT WOULD YOU HAVE US DO? EVEN WE CANNOT TURN BACK THE SUN AND MOON.

NOR NEED WE, HEMUTH, IT IS NOT THE FLOW OF TIME WE MUST REVERSE -- MERELY THE DAMAGE IT HAS DONE TO OUR-SELVES.

AND THE LIVING ORB HAS SHOWN ME A WAY...!

...ON THE SACRIFICIAL ALTER OF THEIR MASTERS.

KROK, LORD OF SOMINUS -- WHOSE SEED SPAWNED ZHERED-NA IN THE WORLD'S BLACK WOMB -- WE CALL UPON THY POWER!

MAY THE AGONIES WE HAVE VISITED UPON THIS CHILD BE THE LABOR OF OUR REBIRTH!

SUCKLE US ON THE CRIMSON MILK THAT FLOWS FROM HER BODY'S WOUNDS!

SHE HAS BORNE THIS SUFFERING THAT OUR BURDEN OF YEARS MIGHT BE LIFTED! NOW, O DEMON-KING, OPEN WIDE HER HEART--

-- TO RECEIVE OUR THANKS!

THUS, A DECREE GOES FORTH FROM THE DARK LORDS TO THE FIVE CITADELS STILL UNDER THEIR RULE: HALF THE YOUNG MEN AND HALF THE YOUNG WOMEN OF THE EMPIRE ARE TO MAKE A PILGRIMMAGE.

IN THE WEEKS THAT FOLLOW, A CEASE-LESS PROCESSION OF UNSPOILED FLESH WINDS ACROSS THE DESERT TO THE SORCERERS' BLACK FORTRESS.

FOR MANY OF THE YOUTHS, IT IS THEIR FIRST GLIMPSE OF KUR. FOR ALL, IT WILL BE THEIR LAST...

THEY HAVE JOURNEYED HERE TO RELINQUISH THEIR LIVES...

WITH EACH HEINOUS ACT OF TORTURE AND MURDER, THE WIZARDS REGAIN SOME SMALL MEASURE OF THEIR LOST VIGOR.

BUT THOUGH THE BLOOD OF THOUSANDS STAINS THE SLAB...

IT IS NOT ENOUGH!

OUR HANDS REMAIN TWISTED LIKE TALONS! THE CENTURIES REMAIN ETCHED IN OUR FACES!

WE ARE OLD MEN-- STILL!!

WE HAVE TAMED OUR SUBJECTS *TOO WELL*, KOTH.

FOR GENERATIONS, THE CITADEL-DWELLERS HAVE HAD NOTHING TO *FEAR* BUT OUR *WRATH* -- NOR ANY *ASPIRATION* BEYOND THE GRATIFICATION OF THEIR DULLED SENSES.

EVEN IN THE FACE OF *DEATH*, THEIR YOUNG HAVE FORGOTTEN *HOW* TO STRUGGLE -- OR *WHY.* THEIR *LISTLESSNESS* BLUNTS THEIR WILL TO LIVE.

AND WHEN ONE'S LIFE IS NOT HELD *PRECIOUS,* ONE'S AGONIES BECOME *TRIVIAL.*

THEY DIE...TOO *EASILY?*

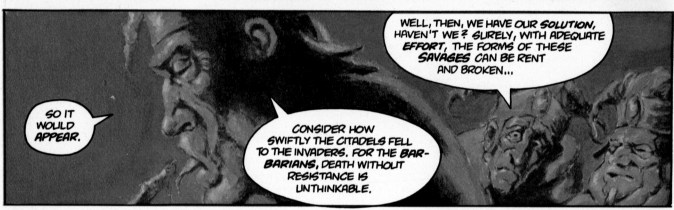

SO IT WOULD APPEAR.

WELL, THEN, WE HAVE OUR *SOLUTION,* HAVEN'T WE? SURELY, WITH ADEQUATE *EFFORT,* THE FORMS OF THESE *SAVAGES* CAN BE RENT AND BROKEN...

CONSIDER HOW SWIFTLY THE CITADELS FELL TO THE INVADERS. FOR THE *BARBARIANS,* DEATH WITHOUT RESISTANCE IS UNTHINKABLE.

BUT *THEY* WILL NOT COME *WILLINGLY,* ZEPHARR. AND WITH OUR FADING POWERS, HOW WOULD WE TAKE THEM *CAPTIVE?*

...AND *THEIR* THROES OUGHT TO PROVIDE US WITH THE *REVITALIZING* ENERGIES WE CRAVE.

NOT "THEM," EEYOD-- *HIM!*

BEHOLD-- THE *IMAGE* THAT FORMS IN THE *LIVING ORB*--!

"*ATH'AGAAR* HIMSELF-- FIERCEST OF THE BARBAR- IAN CHIEFS -- SELF- PROCLAIMED *KING OF EROK!*"

"HE SHALL BE THE ONE WHO *SUFFERS* -- AS NO LIVING THING HAS SUFFERED *BEFORE!*"

FOR ONE GHASTLY MOMENT, ATH'AGAAR GAPES AT THE HIDEOUSLY DIS-FIGURED FACE OF HIS CONCUBINE.

THEN, HIS ANGER ERRUPTS...

DREGS OF HELL!! I'LL CLEAVE YOUR SKULLS FOR THIS--!

ANOTHER SIMPLE GESTURE...

...AND THE BARBARIAN'S BLADE BECOMES A SERPENT, COIL-ING TIGHT ABOUT HIM...

YAARGH

...PINNING HIS ARMS, SQUEEZING THE BREATH FROM HIS LUNGS.

IN MUTE, HELP-LESS ANGUISH, REN WATCHES,...AS HE TOPPLES.

YOUR REIGN IN EROK IS ENDED, ATH'AGAAR.

BUT YOUR TRIBULATIONS HAVE YET TO BEGIN!

YOU--AND YOUR WHORE--WILL BE ACCOMPANY-ING US--

--ON A KIND OF JOURNEY.

"FIRST, WE SHALL RETURN TO *KUR*...

"...AND FROM THERE, PROCEED INTO REALMS *UNCHARTED* IN HUMAN EXPERIENCE."

IN A WAY, BARBAR-IAN, YOU ARE *FORTUNATE.*

PAIN HAS BEEN KNOWN TO OPEN MANY A DOOR TO THE *SPIRIT.*

YOU MIGHT EVEN GAZE UPON THE FACE OF *KAOK* HIM-SELF!

OR, YOU MAY SIMPLY *DIE*-- LIKE THE STUPID SAVAGE YOU ARE.

OBSERVE, ATH'AGAAR, WHAT WE DO TO THE WOMAN.

WE HAVE FAR *GREATER* TORMENTS IN MIND FOR YOU.

DEVILS-- RELEASE HER!!

*T*HEY DO NOT. AND SO, BELLOWING WITH RAGE, SUMMONING EVERY OUNCE OF STRENGTH AND WILL...

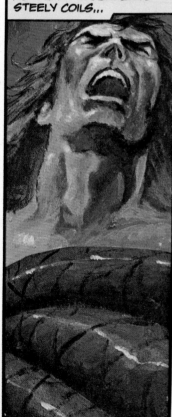

... HE DRAWS A LONG, TOR-TUROUS BREATH, FORCING HIS CHEST TO *EXPAND,* PITTING HIS NAKED BREAST AGAINST THE SERPENT'S STEELY COILS...

...UNTIL ONE OR THE OTHER...

...MUST *BURST!*

FREE HER, SORCERERS-- **NOW!!**--

--BEFORE YOUR WRETCHED **NECKS** GO THE WAY OF YOUR **SERPENT**!

YOU WOULD **THREATEN** US-- HERE, WITHIN THE WALLS OF OUR OWN **STRONG-HOLD**?

HAVE YOU NO **GRASP** OF WHAT FORCES YOU SEEK TO **OPPOSE**?

THERE WAS A TIME, ATH'AGAAR, WHEN **WE FOUR** COULD HAVE STOOD AGAINST THE WHOLE OF YOUR BARBARIC **HORDE**--

--WHEN WE COULD HOLD BACK AN **ARMY** WITH A SIMPLE **SPELL OF CONTAINMENT** SUCH AS THIS!

EVEN IN OUR SAD **DOTAGE** WE CAN BRING TO BEAR FROM THE TIP OF **ONE FINGER** MORE POWER THAN MERE **BRAWN** MIGHT EVER HOPE TO SURMOUNT!

THOSE **FILAMENTS**, SLENDER THOUGH THEY MAY BE, **CANNOT** BE BROKEN BY PHYSICAL MEANS.

STRUGGLE IF YOU **MUST**-- BUT IT WILL NOT ALTER YOUR FATE, OR THE **WOMAN'S**.

NO.!! REN!!

HE ACTUALLY **CARES** FOR HER, KOTH. WE ARE IN THE PRESENCE OF GENUINE **PASSION**.

TOO MANY **CENTURIES** HAVE GONE BY SINCE **WE** HAVE FELT WITH SUCH INTENSITY. I **ENVY** HIM.

I TRUST THAT WON'T **DETER** YOU FROM OUR MEAN LITTLE **TASK**, KOTH.

NO.

MONSTERS!! ARE YOUR **SOULS** AS WITHERED AS YOUR ROTTING **FLESH**??

SHE'S DONE YOU NO **HARM**--!

I AM THE ONE YOU WANT TO **KILL**!

"ON THE CONTRARY," REPLIES EEYOD. "WE WANT YOU *BOTH* -- AND ALL THE *MORE* SO...

"...NOW THAT WE KNOW OF THE *BOND* THAT EXISTS BETWEEN YOU.

"WATCHING HER PERISH BY *DE-GREES* WILL FUEL YOUR *HATRED* FOR US...

"...AND THE FIERCE-NESS OF YOUR *LOATHING* IS PRECISELY WHAT WE *NEED.*"

BEHOLD THE LIGHT THAT GLINTS FROM MY *BLADE,* WOMAN.

IT IS THE LAST *GLIMMER* YOU SHALL EVER *SEE.*

WITH TWO SWIFT SLASHES -- AND NO TRACE OF EMOTION -- EEYOD RENDERS HER *SIGHTLESS.* THEN, EQUALLY ABSENT OF AFFECT, THE OTHERS JOIN IN WHAT BECOMES A PROTRACTED PROCESS OF UNRELENTING *EXCRUCIATION.* TO THEIR GRIM DELIGHT, REN PROVES STRONGER, LESS WILLING TO DIE THAN THEY HAD ANTICIPATED. IT IS *TWILIGHT* OF THE *NEXT DAY...*

...WHEN KOTH FINALLY DELIVERS THE *DEATH-STROKE.*

BY THEN, THERE IS LITTLE *LEFT* OF HER TO *TORMENT.*

NOW, BARBARIAN, COMES THE *JOURNEY* YOU WERE PROMISED -- ACROSS A *VASTNESS* OF AFFLICTION -- AND ON INTO *ETERNITY.*

HER *VITAL FORCE* HAS BEEN EXPENDED AS *AGONY*... AND GREEDILY *DEVOURED* BY THE DARK LORDS.

AS HE IS MADE TO LIE IN REN'S **BLOOD**, AS THE **SHACKLES** CLAMP ABOUT HIS WRISTS AND ANKLES, ATH'AGAAR CONFRONTS THE SOBER FACT THAT THIS TIME THERE WILL BE **NO ESCAPE**. BEREFT OF ALL DEFENSES, EVEN **CLOTHING**, HE IS LIKE A FORLORN **CHILD** --ENTIRELY AT THE MERCY OF THIS PACK OF **SICK OLD MEN**.

AS THE TORMENT PROGRESSES, THE INDIVIDUAL WOUNDS LOSE ALL SIGNIFICANCE. THE PAIN BECOMES AN **ENVIRONMENT**. HE IS ENVELOPED BY IT, **SHEATHED** IN IT-- AND THE ONLY RETREAT FROM IT IS IN THE **MEMORY** OF ANOTHER KIND OF EXISTENCE. SLOWLY, THE MENTAL WALLS THAT SEPARATE HIS PAST FROM THE HERE-AND-NOW BEGIN TO **CRUMBLE**.

HIS SUFFERING IS MADE TO LAST FOR *DAYS*. TIRELESSLY, AND WITH A SURGEON'S *PRECISION*, THE DARK LORDS SUBJECT HIS BODY TO AN UNREMITTING SUCCESSION OF PUNISHMENTS. HE IS *SCORCHED* WITH HOT IRONS AND *SCOURGED* WITH BARBED WHIPS. HE IS GASHED, PUNCTURED, HAMMERED, AND MAULED.

THE BRACING COLD OF THE NORTH, THE HEFT OF HIS FATHER'S *SWORD*, HIS BOYHOOD *TRIUMPHS*, HIS INITIATION INTO *MANHOOD* -- HE RELIVES THEM ALL, AGAIN AND AGAIN, IN A TORRENT...UNTIL EACH RECOLLECTION MELDS WITH ALL THE OTHERS, AND WITH THE *PRESENT* ...AND THEY ALL COME TO FEEL LIKE *PAIN*.

VICTORY IS PAIN.

PAIN IS PAIN.

REN'S EMBRACE IS PAIN.

AND YET, EVEN WITH HIS MIND IN DISARRAY, EVEN WHEN HIS BODY HAS BEEN MAIMED AND MUTILATED ALMOST BEYOND RECOGNITION, ATH'AGAAR CANNOT *SURRENDER* HIS GRIP ON *LIFE*. THE WILL TO *SURVIVE* IS INGRAINED IN HIM TOO DEEPLY. HIS *RAGE* STILL SMOULDERS...AND THE DARK LORDS *SAVOR* IT.

UNTIL, LATE ON THE THIRD NIGHT...

DEATH HOVERS AT YOUR HEAD, ATH'AGAAR --UPON THE TIP OF THIS JEWELED SPIKE.

YOUR ORDEAL IS OVER. THE END IS COME.

NO!... NOT UNTIL I CLAIM MY ...VENGEANCE!... I WILL HUNT YOU DOWN ...SLAY YOUR VERY SOULS...

...IF IT TAKES... ALL ETERNITY!

TO WHICH KOTH RESPONDS WITH A SNEER OF CONTEMPT... AND A HAMMERBLOW.

AT LAST, ATH'AGAAR LIES STILL.

AND EIGHT SATISFIED EYES, ALIVE WITH THE SPARKLE OF YOUTH, GAZE DOWN ON HIS BROKEN BODY.

YOU SHALL HAVE NO REVENGE, BARBARIAN. YOU WERE MEANT TO PERISH AT OUR HANDS. FOR HAD YOU NEVER RIDDEN INTO OUR MIDST, OUR EMPIRE WOULD SURELY HAVE FALLEN. AND HAD YOU LOVED LIFE LESS, YOU WOULD NOT NOW BE DEAD.

SAVE YOUR PREACHMENTS, KOTH... UNTIL THE BRUTE IS ON THE PYRE.

ZEPHARR IS RIGHT, KOTH. THE EFFECT WILL FADE IF KAOK'S HOSTS ARE DENIED THEIR FEAST.

JUDGE NOT THE GODS' APPETITES BY YOUR OWN, HEMUTH.

THEY DO NOT HUNGER ALL THE TIME.

HEMUTH GASPS...

...NOT AT THE INSULT, AS THE OTHERS FIRST PRESUME...

FOR EACH PHENOMENON THAT OCCURS IN THE *MATERIAL WORLD* HAS CONSEQUENCES FAR *BEYOND* IT. BE IT THE FALLING OF A RAINDROP OR OF A CULTURE, ITS EFFECTS RIPPLE ACROSS *EVERY PLANE OF REALITY.*

SOME, LIKE THE RAINDROP, VIBRATE IN *HARMONY* WITH THE COSMIC ORDER.

BUT THE SHRIEKING OF A HUNDRED THOUSAND ENTITIES USHERED PRE-MATURELY TO THEIR DEATHS PRODUCES *DISCORD* IN THE *SPHERE OF SOULS.*

THEIR SPIRIT-VOICES HOWL AS ONE: *"PUNISH THE SORCERERS! LET THEM KNOW NO PEACE UNTIL THEY HAVE PAID FOR THEIR ATROCITIES!"*

THE COSMOS CONVULSES--AND THE DARK LORDS ARE SPAT BACK INTO THE *REALM OF MATTER*, INTO A CYCLE OF *DEATH AND REBIRTH* FROM WHICH NO RELEASE IS POSSIBLE, UNTIL THEIR EVIL HAS BEEN *EXPUNGED* ...OR THEIR SOULS ANNIHILATED.

THERE IS NO *HARSHER* PENALTY THE UNIVERSE MAY EXACT.

YET TWO *RENEGADE SOULS*, HALF-CRAZED WITH PAIN AND HATE, UNABLE TO *ACCEPT* THEIR INTEGRATION INTO THE *ALL*, TEAR LOOSE OF THE COSMIC FABRIC AND WILLINGLY *FOLLOW*--

--SEEKING *REVENGE*--AND ONE ANOTHER.

A GULF OF MORE THAN *ELEVEN MILLENIA* STANDS BETWEEN THE DES-TRUCTION OF KUR AND THE *PRESENT*. DURING THESE CENTURIES, ATH'AGAAR, REN, AND THE DARK LORDS ALL LIVE INNUMERABLE LIFETIMES--SOME AS BRIEF AS A *MOTH'S*, OTHERS AS LONG AS A *REDWOOD'S*.

THEIR SOULS ARE *SCATTERED* OVER CONTINENTS AND SEAS, AND ACROSS THE VASTNESS OF *SPACE*.

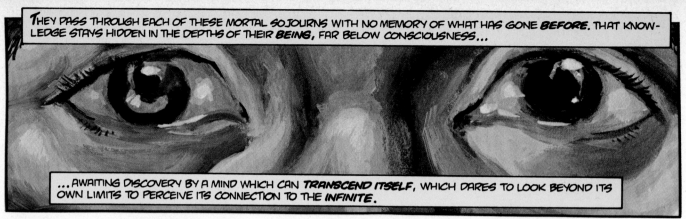

THEY PASS THROUGH EACH OF THESE MORTAL SOJOURNS WITH NO MEMORY OF WHAT HAS GONE *BEFORE*. THAT KNOW-LEDGE STAYS HIDDEN IN THE DEPTHS OF THEIR *BEING*, FAR BELOW CONSCIOUSNESS...

...AWAITING DISCOVERY BY A MIND WHICH CAN *TRANSCEND ITSELF*, WHICH DARES TO LOOK BEYOND ITS OWN LIMITS TO PERCEIVE ITS CONNECTION TO THE *INFINITE*.

IN ALL THEIR MYRIAD LIFE-TIMES, HOWEVER, ONLY *ONE SOUL* AMONG THEM ACHIEVES THIS GOAL.

IRONICALLY, IT IS THAT OF *KOTH*.

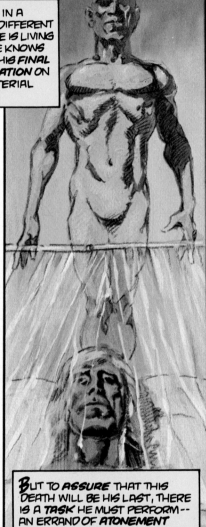

REBORN IN A VASTLY DIFFERENT FORM, HE IS LIVING WHAT HE KNOWS MAY BE HIS *FINAL INCARNATION* ON THE MATERIAL PLANE.

BUT TO *ASSURE* THAT THIS DEATH WILL BE HIS LAST, THERE IS A *TASK* HE MUST PERFORM-- AN ERRAND OF *ATONEMENT* FOR CRIMES PAST.

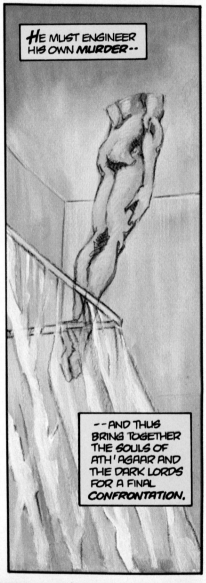

HE MUST ENGINEER HIS OWN *MURDER*--

--AND THUS BRING TOGETHER THE SOULS OF ATH'AGAAR AND THE DARK LORDS FOR A FINAL *CONFRONTATION*.

ONLY IN THIS WAY WILL THEIR EONS-OLD CONFLICT EVER BE *RESOLVED*.

BY AN IMMENSE EFFORT OF WILL, HE SEPARATES HIS *EIDOLON* --HIS ASTRAL FORCE-- FROM HIS PHYSICAL SHELL.

...AND PROJECTS IT ON A JOURNEY BEYOND THE MORTAL VEIL, INTO THE CONTINUUM OF *PURE SPIRIT*...

...THE **VOID INDIGO!**

THROUGH THIS HORIZONLESS, LIQUID SPACE FROM WHICH ALL THINGS--MATERIAL AND SPIRITUAL--ORIGINATE, THREADS THE *GREAT CHAIN OF BEING.*

EACH PERFECT, PEARL-LIKE BEAD ALONG ITS INFINITE LENGTH GLIMMERS WITH THE LIGHT OF A SOUL. FROM ITS *POSITION* ON THE CHAIN CAN BE DETERMINED THE *CONDITION* OF THAT SOUL AND ITS *LOCATION* IN THE COSMOS.

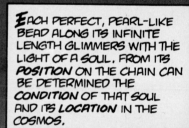

REN AND THE FORMER DARK LORDS RESIDE ON *EARTH.*

ATH'AGAAR, THOUGH, IS...*ELSEWHERE.*

HE COMMANDS A **SPACE FLEET** NOW, NOT A HORDE ON HORSEBACK. HE FLEES A **DYING STAR**, NOT A **GLACIER**, AND HIS OPPONENTS ARE THE DRONES OF **TECHNOLOGICAL WIZARDS**.

THE TWO ARMIES DESTROY ONE ANOTHER NOT WITH SWORDS AND SPEARS, BUT WITH **PARTICLE BEAMS**.

AND YET THE WAR IS THE **SAME** ONE HE FOUGHT SO LONG AGO ON **EARTH**-- FOR THE SURVIVAL OF A RACE, AGAINST THE WILL OF A TYRANNICAL **EMPIRE**.

WHEN THE FIRST EXCHANGE OF FIRE IS OVER, ONLY **TWO** OF THE SPACECRAFT REMAIN **INTACT**. ONE IS THE MASSIVE **IMPERIAL FLAGSHIP**.

THE OTHER HARBORS THE SOUL OF **ATH'AGAAR**...OR SO THE EIDOLON BELIEVES.

HE PASSES THROUGH THE HULL, INTO THE ONE-MAN FIGHTER, TO MAKE **CERTAIN**.

BEFORE HE **ACTS**, HE MUST BANISH ALL **DOUBT** THAT THIS IS THE REINCARNATION OF HIS ANCIENT FOE.

AS IF SENSING THE NUMINOUS **PRESENCE** AT HIS BACK...

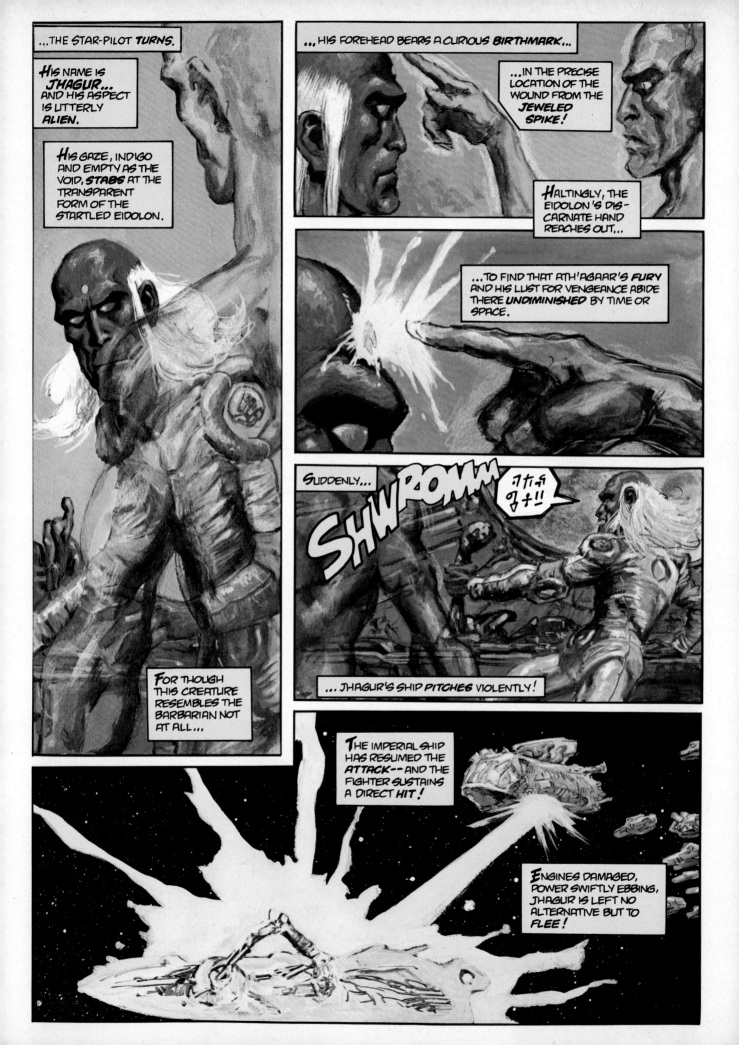

THE VOICE OF KOTH'S SOUL -- CHANTING TELEPATHICALLY--!

THE EIDOLON CANNOT PERMIT JHAGUR THIS VICTORY. THAT WOULD MEAN THE ALIEN WARRIOR'S ESCAPE...

...AND THAT WOULD THWART THE EIDOLON'S OWN OBJECTIVE.

FOR A FATEFUL INSTANT, GRIPPED BY AN UNEXPLAINABLE RAGE, JHAGUR HESITATES...

...LONG ENOUGH FOR THE ENEMY CRAFT TO RETURN HIS FIRE.

AND THAT IS HOW THE BATTLE ENDS.

TRAILING RED-HOT METAL, JHAGUR'S SHIP PLUMMETS TOWARD THE PLANET BELOW...

...TOWARD THE EARTH!

AND, AS THE EIDOLON INTENDED, IT CRASHES ON THE VERY DESERT WHERE THE CITADEL OF EROK ONCE STOOD.

THE SOUL OF ATH'AGAAR HAS RETURNED--TO THE LAND OF ENCHANTMENT OUR PRESENT CENTURY CALLS...NEW MEXICO.

FOR LONG MOMENTS AFTER THE DEAFENING *IMPACT*, THE DESERT LIES TRANQUIL, SAVE FOR THE SIBILANT HISS OF SIZZLING METAL.

THEN...

NOTHING REMAINS OF THE SHIP BUT CHARRED, TWISTED DEBRIS.

JHAGUR IS STRANDED...

...A TATTERDEMALION FROM THE STARS, WITH NO MEANS TO CONTACT HIS BRETHREN HALF-A-GALAXY AWAY...FAR BEYOND THIS NITROGEN-BLUE SKY.

HE WILL FIND A WAY, HE TELLS HIMSELF...IN *TIME*.

UNTIL THEN, HE MUST *SURVIVE*.

HE SHAMBLES INTO THE WASTELAND, IN SEARCH OF SHELTER.

QUIMBY, NEW MEXICO:

DAYS AND NIGHTS OF AIMLESS PERAMBULATION FINALLY LEAD JHAGUR TO THIS EVIDENCE THAT THE PLANET MAY SUPPORT SAPIENT LIFE.

WARILY, AND WITH CONSIDERABLE SKEPTICISM, HE INSPECTS THE BOXLIKE DWELLINGS.

IN ONE AFTER ANOTHER, HE DISCOVERS ESSENTIALLY THE THE SAME SCENE:

HA HA HA

GROUPINGS OF LATERALLY BISYMMETRICAL LIFE-FORMS, USUALLY BIPEDAL, GATHERED IN A SINGLE ROOM,...

HEEE HA HA

...THEIR ATTENTION RIVETED ON A PRIMITIVE, ONE-WAY TELECOMUNICATIONS DEVICE.

HO-HOO AHA

ONLY DETAILS—THE SPECIMENS' NUMBER, GENDER, ARRANGEMENT, SPECIFIC GRAVITY—VARY.

PROTO-SENTIENTS...!

NEITHER INTELLIGENCE NOR TECHNOLOGY HAS EVOLVED SUFFICIENTLY HERE TO ASSIST HIS RETURN TO HIS PEOPLE.

HE CONTINUES HIS EXPLORATIONS, DISHEARTENED.

NEAR THE EDGE OF TOWN, HE COMES UPON AN EXCEPTION:

A LONE, DECREPIT HABITATION WHERE THE FLICKERING LIGHT AND TINNY VOICE OF THE SAD LITTLE SCREEN DO NOT GREET HIS APPROACH.

INTRIGUED, HE DRAWS CLOSER...

...HOPING TO LEARN HOW THESE BEINGS BEHAVE WHEN NOT IN A STATE OF ELECTRON-ICALLY-INDUCED TORPOR.

INSIDE, A MALE AND FEMALE "PROTO-SENTIENT", LIMBS INTERTWINED, ROLL AND JOUNCE NOISILY ABOUT ON A CUSHIONED RECTANGULAR PLATFORM.

EROGENIC FRENZY.

JHAGUR HAS WITNESSED SIMILARLY FRANTIC MATING ACTIVITY ON OTHER WORLDS, AMONG OTHER BACKWARD SPECIES, BUT IT NEVER FAILS TO FASCINATE -- AND APPALL.

FOR GEBURANS, COMPOSURE, PRE-CISION, AND SILENCE CON-STITUTE THE HALLMARKS OF THE ART.

HE OBSERVES THE ANTICS TO THEIR PREDICTABLE CON-CLUSION, THEN TURNS TO LEAVE... HIS MOOD ODDLY LIGHTENED.

THIS PLEASES HIM. HIS EXILE MAY PROVE MARGINALLY MORE BEARABLE IF THIS WORLD CAN PROVIDE AN OCCASIONAL ENTERTAINMENT.

HOWEVER, EVEN THIS MEAGER CONSOLATION IS SHORT-LIVED.

NOOOOO

CHARLIE'S HEAVY BOOT RISES AGAIN, BUT AS IT BEGINS ITS DESCENT TO LINETTE'S FACE...

... A BOLT OF INDIGO ENERGY FLASHES FROM THE ALIEN'S EYES...

... AND INTERCEPTS IT.

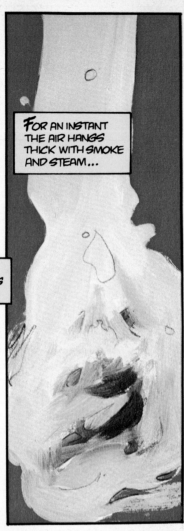

FOR AN INSTANT THE AIR HANGS THICK WITH SMOKE AND STEAM...

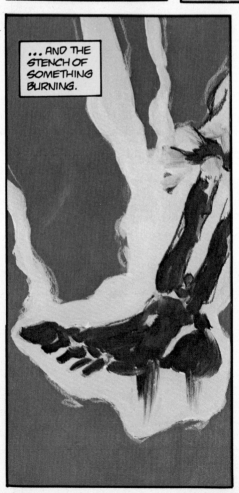

... AND THE STENCH OF SOMETHING BURNING.

CHARLIE TOPPLES, HIS FULL WEIGHT FALLING ON THE SKELETAL FOOT.

THE BONES SPLINTER.

AUDIBLY.

ohhh, god ...oh, jesus...

the pain...

oh god... it hurts... unnnh...

Y-YOU BURNT THE SKIN CLEAN **OFF** 'IM!

HOW-- COULD ANYBODY --**DO** SUCH A THING--?!

HE-HE'S GONNA BE A **CRIPPLE**--THE REST OF HIS **LIFE**, AIN'T HE--?

AT THIS THOUGHT, HER **HORROR** AT THE GRISLY SIGHT...

...GIVES WAY TO A SOMEWHAT CRAZED, IRRESPONSIBLE **GIGGLE**.

WHAT'RE YOU **SNIGGERIN'** AT, YOU MORONIC **BITCH**?

G-GET ME A DOCTOR--**HURRY**! KEYS'RE IN THE **TRUCK**--!!

CAN'T, CHARLIE-- I GOT PLACES TO **GO**. CALL THE WIFE AN' KIDS, WHY DON'TCHA?

THEY'RE IN EARSHOT --**REMEM- BER**?

OH, AN' THANKS FOR THE **TIP** ABOUT THE **KEYS**, HEAR?

YOU BETTER BLOW TOWN, TOO, RED--IF YOU KNOW WHAT'S GOOD FOR YOU.

NOBODY'S GONNA BELIEVE CHARLIE TRIED TO **ROB** ME. I'M JUST THE LOCAL HARLOT--

--**HE'S** THE DEPUTY SHERIFF!

AS THE ENGINE COUGHS AND RATTLES TO LIFE.

GO. WITH YOU.

HUH?! **OH**, NO! I'M STRICTLY A **SOLO ACT**, RED! I COULDN'T--

AAAH, WHAT THE HELL? GUESS I **OWE** YOU ONE, DON'T I ...?

SKIPPIN' OUT IN A STOLEN TRUCK--WITH A DUDE THAT LOOKS LIKE THE **DEVIL** HIMSELF--**WHOO**!

I ALWAYS HAVE BEEN A **LITTLE** BIT NUTS --BUT **THIS** TAKES THE CAKE AN' HALF THE **PIE** ...!

I'M GONNA STAY ON THE *BACK ROADS*--STEER CLEAR OF THE INTERSTATES--IF THAT'S OKAY WITH YOU.

BY THE WAY, I'M *LINETTE CUMPSTON.* YOU GOT A NAME?

JHAGUR.

UH-HUH. FIRST NAME *"MICK,"* NO DOUBT.

MICK.

FUN-*NEE.* WELL, MICK, YOU GOT ANY WAY TO MAKE YOURSELF LOOK LESS *BRITISH*-- NOW'S THE TIME!

ELSEWISE, I MIGHT HAVETA PUT A *BAG* OVER YOUR HEAD!

SEE, THERE'S COPS ON *THIS* ROAD, TOO--NOT MANY, BUT *SOME*--

--AN' YOU'RE NOT EXACTLY GONNA BE HARD TO *IDENTIFY.* SAVVY?

JHAGUR TOUCHES ANOTHER JEWEL-LIKE STUD ON HIS BELT...

...ACTIVATING ITS PHOTO-CHROMATIC CAMOUFLAGING FUNCTION.

LINETTE GAPES, AS HE SEEMS TO DISSOLVE IN SHIFTING PATTERNS OF REFRACTION.

A MOMENT LATER, HIS FEATURES SLIP BACK INTO SHARP RESOLUTION...

...HIS TRUE NATURE UTTERLY CONCEALED BY A TECHNOLOGICAL FORM OF PROTECTIVE COLORATION.

MICK?

JHAGUR?

GOD ALMIGHTY DOG...! *HA HA HAHAHAAHOOH*

...?

LACKING EDUCATIONAL CREDENTIALS (WHICH LINETTE NEGLECTED TO PURCHASE) AND WITH A MARKEDLY "FOREIGN" ACCENT TO HIS ENGLISH, JHAGUR FINDS HIS OPPORTUNITIES LIMITED.

HE DRIFTS FROM ONE STRENUOUS JOB TO THE NEXT, ACCRUING MORE IN MUSCLE MASS THAN IN WAGES.

OVER TIME, THE SLENDER STAR-PILOT DEVELOPS A HARDIER PHYSIQUE, TOUGHENED BY EXPOSURE TO THE ELEMENTS.

EVENINGS, WHILE LINETTE DISPENSES BEER AND CHEER, HE STAYS ALONE AT HOME, ENGROSSED IN STUDY. HE READS OMNIVOROUSLY: DARWIN AND THE BIBLE, EINSTEIN AND VELIKOVSKY, HOMER AND HAROLD ROBBINS.

THE COMBINATION OF HARD WORK AND INTELLECTUAL EXERTION AGREES WITH HIM, AS DO LINETTE'S UNDEMANDING COMPANIONSHIP AND HER ALMOST SIMPLE-MINDED ACCEPTANCE OF HIS ALIEN-NESS.

AS HIS EXILE STRETCHES INTO MONTHS, JHAGUR CONCEDES THE POSSIBILITY THAT HE MAY SPEND THE REST OF HIS LIFE ON EARTH. HAVING ADMITTED THIS, HIS ADJUSTMENT PROCEEDS WITH SURPRISING EASE.

THE PLANET'S CUSTOMS AND CULTURE, ITS PEOPLE AND TOPOGRAPHY--EVEN ITS BLUE SKY--ALL SEEM TO "RESONATE" IN SOME HERETOFORE UNVISITED CHAMBER OF HIS PERSONALITY.

WHEN HE DOFFS HIS BELT--AND WITH IT HIS CAMOUFLAGE--TO CHANGE OR SHOWER OR SLEEP--LINETTE TAKES THE TRANSFORMATION IN STRIDE, ACKNOWLEDGING IT MERELY WITH A CONSPIRATORIAL GIGGLE.

THEY FORM A BOND OF MUTUAL ACCEPTANCE AND TRUST--LIKE THAT BETWEEN A SISTER AND BROTHER--WHICH IS ALMOST WITHOUT RESERVATION.

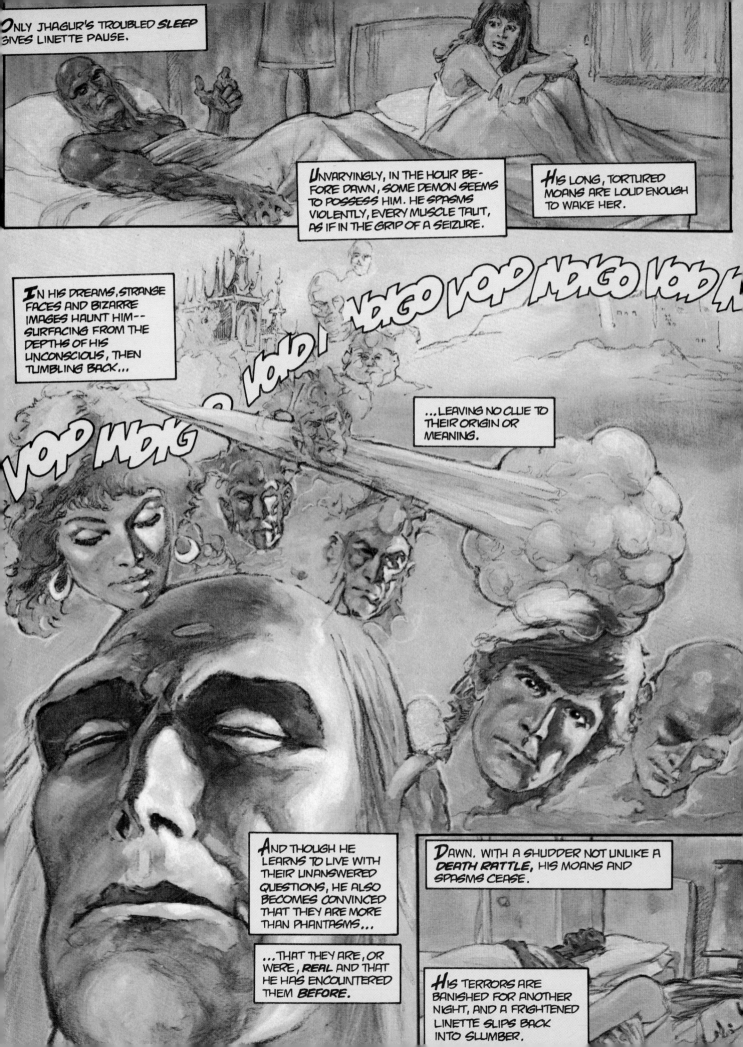

ONLY JHAGUR'S TROUBLED **SLEEP** GIVES LINETTE PAUSE.

UNVARYINGLY, IN THE HOUR BEFORE DAWN, SOME DEMON SEEMS TO POSSESS HIM. HE SPASMS VIOLENTLY, EVERY MUSCLE TAUT, AS IF IN THE GRIP OF A SEIZURE.

HIS LONG, TORTURED MOANS ARE LOUD ENOUGH TO WAKE HER.

IN HIS DREAMS, STRANGE FACES AND BIZARRE IMAGES HAUNT HIM-- SURFACING FROM THE DEPTHS OF HIS UNCONSCIOUS, THEN TUMBLING BACK...

...LEAVING NO CLUE TO THEIR ORIGIN OR MEANING.

AND THOUGH HE LEARNS TO LIVE WITH THEIR UNANSWERED QUESTIONS, HE ALSO BECOMES CONVINCED THAT THEY ARE MORE THAN PHANTASMS...

...THAT THEY ARE, OR WERE, **REAL** AND THAT HE HAS ENCOUNTERED THEM **BEFORE**.

DAWN, WITH A SHUDDER NOT UNLIKE A **DEATH RATTLE**, HIS MOANS AND SPASMS CEASE.

HIS TERRORS ARE BANISHED FOR ANOTHER NIGHT, AND A FRIGHTENED LINETTE SLIPS BACK INTO SLUMBER.

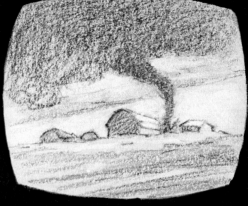

"...U.S. MARINE POSITIONS IN LEBANON WERE AGAIN SUBJECTED TO HEAVY ARTILLERY FIRE BY MUSLIM GUERILLAS TODAY. CASUALTIES WERE DESCRIBED AS 'LIGHT'..."

"...TORNADO TORE A SWATCH OF DESTRUCTION THROUGH SOUTH-EAST MISSOURI YESTERDAY, DEVASTATING A 20-MILE STRIP OF HOMES AND BUSINESSES..."

"...WHILE, ACCORDING TO ECONOMIST MYRON MOOKE: 'BY THE YEAR 2000, FEDERAL DEFICITS MAY RISE BEYOND THE LEVEL AT WHICH EVEN PUNISHING TAXATION WOULD BE SUFFICIENT TO...'"

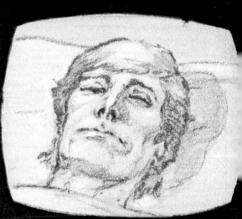

"...AND A SAD STORY OUT OF LOS ANGELES. PENTATHALON GOLD MEDALIST DAVID TREPPER LIES NEAR DEATH IN DORMAN-CONNER MEDICAL CENTER, AS HIS TWO-YEAR BATTLE WITH MYASTHENIA GRAVIS, A DEGENERATIVE NEURO-MUSCULAR DISEASE, NEAR ITS TRAGIC CONCLUSION.

"DEBBIE TOKUGAWA SPOKE WITH THE ATHLETE'S MOTHER:

"IS DAVID CONSCIOUS, MRS. TREPPER?"

"HE'S MEDITATING. HE'S MADE A PRACTICE OF IT SINCE HE LEARNED HE HAD THE DISEASE."

"CAN HE SPEAK?"

"HE DOESN'T CONVERSE. HE CHANTS. RELIGIOUS THINGS: 'VOID INDIGO... ATH'AGAAR.' THEY MEAN SOMETHING TO HIM, I THINK."

THAT FACE...

...FROM THE DREAMS!

MICK? YOU'RE NOT LEAVIN', ARE YOU? I ALMOST GOT DINNER FIXED!

HOLD YOUR GODDAMN HORSES! WHAT'S THE RUSH--?!

I HAVE TO PAY A CALL ON AN OLD ACQUAINTANCE--

--BEFORE HE DIES.

DORMAN-CONNER MEDICAL CENTER:

MR. TREPPER IS IN ROOM 1132...

...BUT HE'S ONLY SEEING FAMILY AND CLOSE FRIENDS.

I UNDER-STAND.

I MAY BE HIS OLDEST FRIEND ON EARTH.

I-I BEG YOUR PARDON? MY SON DOESN'T KNOW YOU...!

STAND AWAY FROM THE DOOR, PLEASE.

I AM GOING INSIDE.

I THINK HE DOES...!

OH GOD ...GUARD! GUARD!

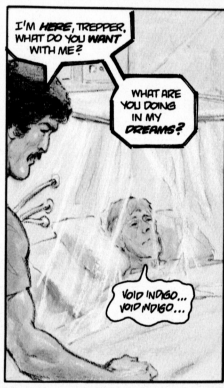

I'M HERE, TREPPER, WHAT DO YOU WANT WITH ME?

WHAT ARE YOU DOING IN MY DREAMS?

VOID INDIGO... VOID INDIGO...

...VOID... IND!...

ATH... ASAAR...

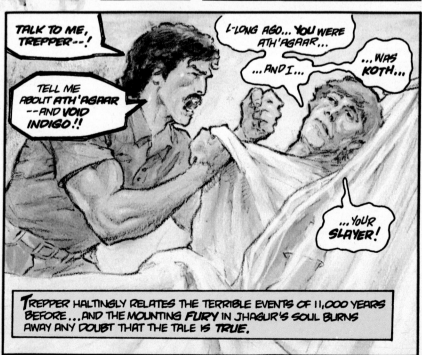

TALK TO ME, TREPPER--!

TELL ME ABOUT ATH'ASAAR --AND VOID INDIGO!!

L-LONG AGO... YOU WERE ATH'ASAAR...

...AND I...

...WAS KOTH...

...YOUR SLAYER!

TREPPER HALTINGLY RELATES THE TERRIBLE EVENTS OF 11,000 YEARS BEFORE...AND THE MOUNTING FURY IN JHAGUR'S SOUL BURNS AWAY ANY DOUBT THAT THE TALE IS TRUE.

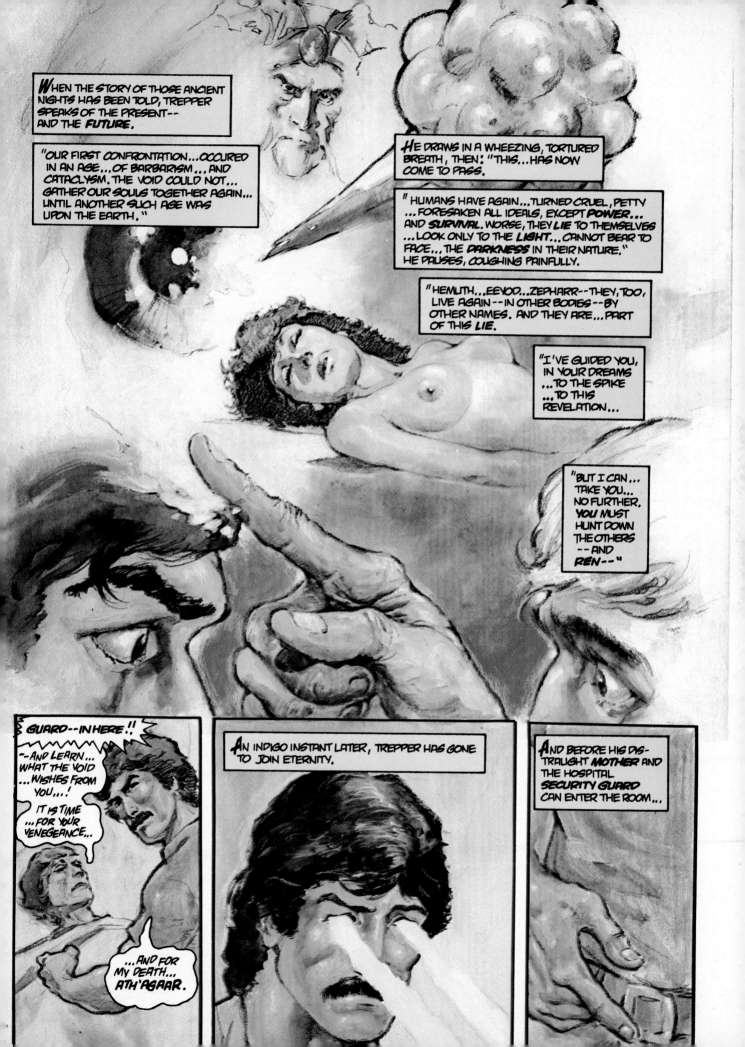

...THE FACE OF HIS ASSAILANT HAS BEEN CONCEALED BY THE *TRUTH*.

EEAAGH!

OH, GAWD --THE *SMELL!* I'M GONNA BE --÷urrgh÷

STOP HIM! *STOP THAT MAN!!*

BUT THE GUARD IS TOO *NAUSEOUS*--

--AND THE REST OF THE STAFF TOO *STUNNED* BY THE INTRUDER'S BIZARRE APPEARANCE!

BY THE TIME THEY REGAIN THEIR *COMPOSURE*, JHAGUR IS DOWN THE STAIRS... OUT OF THE BUILDING...

...ACROSS THE PARKING LOT,...AND LOST IN THE SHADOWS OF THE NIGHT.

SIX MINUTES LATER, AND FIVE BLOCKS AWAY, MICHAEL JAGGER CATCHES A BUS HOME TO NORTH HOLLYWOOD.

Logo Design **Ron Fontes** • Lettering **Andy Kubert** • Editors **Laurie Sutton & Archie Goodwin** • Editor in Chief **Jim Shooter**